'I stare at t
poured n
I think: ca
poison that stimulates
the heart. There are
plenty of instances
of people killing
themselves with
coffee, hundreds and
thousands of them.
Caffeine is a deadly
poison, maybe
almost as deadly
as morphine. Why
didn't it ever occur
to me before: coffee
is my friend!'

HANS FALLADA
Born 21 July 1893, Greifswald, Germany
Died 5 February 1947, Berlin, Germany

'Short Treatise on the Joys of Morphinism' and 'Three Years of Life' are published here in English for the very first time. Both were first published posthumously in German, in the form translated here, in 1997 under the title *Drei Jahre Kein Mensch: Erlebtes, Erfahrenes, Erfundenes*.

ALSO PUBLISHED BY PENGUIN BOOKS
Alone in Berlin

HANS FALLADA

Short Treatise on the Joys of Morphinism

TRANSLATED BY MICHAEL HOFMANN

PENGUIN BOOKS

PENGUIN CLASSICS

Published by the Penguin Group
Penguin Books Ltd, 80 Strand, London WC2R ORL, England
Penguin Group (USA) Inc., 375 Hudson Street, New York, New York 10014, USA
Penguin Group (Canada), 90 Eglinton Avenue East, Suite 700, Toronto, Ontario,
Canada M4P 2Y3 (a division of Pearson Penguin Canada Inc.)
Penguin Ireland, 25 St Stephen's Green, Dublin 2, Ireland (a division of Penguin Books Ltd)
Penguin Group (Australia), 250 Camberwell Road, Camberwell, Victoria 3124, Australia
(a division of Pearson Australia Group Pty Ltd)
Penguin Books India Pvt Ltd, 11 Community Centre, Panchsheel Park,
New Delhi – 110 017, India
Penguin Group (NZ), 67 Apollo Drive, Rosedale, North Shore 0632, New Zealand
(a division of Pearson New Zealand Ltd)
Penguin Books (South Africa) (Pty) Ltd, 24 Sturdee Avenue, Rosebank, Johannesburg 2196,
South Africa
Penguin Books Ltd, Registered Offices: 80 Strand, London WC2R ORL, England

www.penguin.com

This translation first published in Penguin Classics 2011

3

Copyright © Aufbau-Verlagsgruppe GmbH, Berlin, 1997, 2005
Translation copyright © Michael Hofmann, 2011

All rights reserved

Typeset by Jouve (UK), Milton Keynes
Printed in England by Clays Ltd, St Ives plc

ISBN: 978-0-141-19580-3

www.greenpenguin.co.uk

Penguin Books is committed to a sustainable future
for our business, our readers and our planet.
The book in your hands is made from paper
certified by the Forest Stewardship Council.

Contents

NB: All footnotes are the translator's own

Short Treatise on the Joys of Morphinism

I

All of this happened in that first terrible time in Berlin when I was drowning in morphine.[1]

Things had gone okay for me for a few weeks, I had collared a big supply of benzene, which was the name we gave the stuff amongst ourselves, and that relieved me of the addict's worst fear, the fear of running out of drug. Then, as my supply dwindled away, my rate of consumption increased; what I had in mind, I suppose,

1. An apt and suggestive echo of the beginning of Knut Hamsun's great first novel *Hunger* (1880), to which I have adapted my beginning. It goes (in Robert Bly's 1967 translation): 'All of this happened while I was walking around starving in Christiania – that strange city no one escapes from until it has left its mark on him . . .' The events Fallada describes happened – *mas o menos* – in early 1919.

was for once getting really full, with no half-measures, and then – a clean break. Some time a different life would have to begin, and if I had some proper momentum I'd be able to see myself through the sudden stop. At least, I'd heard of others who had managed that way.

But when I woke up on the designated morning, staring into the void, I knew I had to have morphine at any price. My whole body was painfully jittery, my hands shook, I was full of a crazy thirst, not just in my mouth and throat, but in every cell of my body.

I picked up the telephone and called Wolf. I wanted to catch him off-guard, so, with a faltering voice, I croaked out: 'Have you got any benzene? Hurry! I'm dying!'

And fell back on to the pillows, groaning. A deep and solemn feeling of relief, an anticipation of the enjoyment to come, took the edge off my suffering: Wolf would come by car, I have the syringe in my hand – I can already feel the stab of the needle, and then life will be beautiful again.

The telephone trilled, and I heard Wolf saying: 'Why did you hang up so fast? I can't bring you any benzene, I haven't got any myself. I was going to go hunting for some.'

'One injection, Wolf, just one injection, otherwise I'm going to die.'

'But I told you I'm out.'

'You've got some left. I know you have.'

'I swear I don't.'

'I can tell by your voice that you've just had some. You sound full.'

'Last night at one a.m. was the last time.'

'Well, I've had none since eleven. Hurry, Wolf.'

'But it's no good. Tell you what, why don't you come with me. I've got a reliable pharmacy. Take a car, we'll meet at the Alex[2] at nine.'

'And you're not going to stiff me? Swear!'

'Don't be silly, Hans! Nine o'clock at the Alex.'

I get up very slowly, getting dressed is incredibly hard, my joints are quivery and weak, the feeling of assurance is gone, my body doesn't believe I'm going to be able to resupply it.

I happen to look at the calendar, and see that today's an ill-starred day. That makes me sit down in my chair and have a little cry to myself. I'm suffering so badly, and I can sense I'm going to suffer much worse in the course of the day, and I feel so weak. Why can't I just die! But I've known the answer to that for a long time, it's because I'm too much of a coward, I'll have to stick it out, I've got no alternative but to lie there

2. The Alexanderplatz, heart of the eastern part of Berlin.

prostrated and whimpering in front of fate, and beg it not to hurt me.

Then my landlady comes along and says something comforting to me, but I don't interrupt my crying for her, I just wave her away. But she's still talking, gradually I understand I'm being told that I burned holes in my bed last night again with cigarettes. I hand her some money, and since she leaves me alone, it must have been enough.

But I still don't go, even though it's nearly nine o'clock, I stare at the coffee I poured myself, and I think: caffeine is a poison that stimulates the heart. There are plenty of instances of people killing themselves with coffee, hundreds and thousands of them. Caffeine is a deadly poison, maybe almost as deadly as morphine. Why didn't it ever occur to me before: coffee is my friend!

And I gulp down one, two cups. I sit there for a minute, staring into space, and wait. I go on trying to kid myself, even though I know I've been deliberately trying to pull the wool over my eyes. Inevitably, my stomach refuses to keep even that watery coffee down. I can feel my whole body shake and a cold sweat come over me, I need to get up, I am shaken with cramps, and then sour bursts of bile. 'I'm going to die,' I whisper to myself, and stare into space.

A little later I've recovered to the degree that I can get up and take a few steps, and then I finish washing, go out on the street and hail a cab. Wolf's never early anyway.

2

I'm lucky, he's still waiting. I can see right away that he's hungry too, his pupils are dilated, his cheeks are sunken and his nose has some extra definition.

It turns out that he hasn't yet faked the prescriptions he needs to take to the pharmacy. Even though he was as jumpy as me, he couldn't settle to it at home. But he has his little valise with him and can show up in the pharmacy with a reasonable impersonation of a morphine addict just passing through the city on his way to a sanatorium. He's been round the block a few times, he knows better than to forge Berlin prescriptions that can be checked with a simple phone call.

We go into a post office, where we fill out a dozen prescriptions. We review the handwriting, and throw out three prescriptions that strike us as insufficiently doctorly-illegible.

Then we agree on the part of town where we're going to hunt. As Wolf's tame pharmacy is in the East, it makes sense to hunt there, even though the West in general has more going for it. The better-off class of person who lives in the West is more likely to be able to fund an expensive vice like morphinism than the working people in the East. The pharmacies in the West are already adjusting to their clientele.

We go by cab. Wolf has the driver pull over a little way from the nearest pharmacy and he hobbles off, looking sick and wretched. I lean back in the upholstery. Wolf has written Solution, and it'll take him fifteen minutes.

So I'll have benzene in fifteen minutes! High time too, my body is feeling weaker and weaker, I have these terrible pains in my stomach, which is crying out for its drug. I lean back, I shut my eyes, I try to think about how lovely it will be to have the needle in fifteen minutes. A matter of minutes, a few tiny tiny instants, really no time at all, and a deep and holy peace will flow into my joints, and life will be beautiful, and I will be able to dream about palaces and girls. They will all be mine, the most beautiful girls in the world, I'll just have to flash them a smile . . . Morphine makes it possible, I just close my eyes, and the whole world belongs to me.

What's keeping Wolf? How can it take them so long to brew up this bit of stuff? But I'm not going to complain, it's a good sign that he's not back right away, it means they really are making up the medicine. If he's back fast, it can only mean they've rejected the prescription. I'm going to have morphine in a minute! And I lay the syringe on the seat next to me, to have it ready.

Here's Wolf now. I can tell at a glance he hasn't got it. He tells the driver the next address, sits down next to me and shuts his eyes, and I notice he's panting, wiping the sweat off his brow with his hand.

'They're no human beings in there, they're beasts, they're filth! How can they inflict such suffering on innocent people? I had to plead with them not to call the cops.'

'I thought this was a tame pharmacy?'

'The old apothecary wasn't there, there was one of those young chaps instead. They're all so sharp they cut themselves, you know the type.'

'I can't keep going much longer, Wolf. Shouldn't we maybe call it quits, and check ourselves into an institution?'

'Do you think they'll give you any? You'll wind up in a padded cell and left to scream to your heart's content. Bobby hanged himself eight times one night from his bed-leg; in the end the warders left him till he was almost blue, so that it would take him a bit longer to get his strength up to do it again. But they still didn't give him any.'

The cab stops. Wolf tries again. While he's gone, I resolve to come off morphine by myself. If I am to rely on Wolf and his pharmacies, I'll never get my eight fixes a day.[3] I'll just have to lessen my dose, I can manage that. Only now, I need two or three fixes right off, just to get good and full.

Wolf is back already, gives the next address, and we set off.

'Nothing?'

'Nothing!'

It's looking bleak. And outside people are running around with their heads full of plans, looking forward to stuff, and there are flowers and girls and books and theatres. All of it doesn't exist for me. I'm thinking that Berlin has hundreds of pharmacies, and every one of them has stacks of morphine, and I'm not getting any of it. I'm suffering, even though it would be so easy to make me happy, the pharmacist has only to turn a key . . . I don't mind paying, I'm happy to give him all the money I have.

Wolf moves on.

Suddenly it occurs to me that this repeated parking next to pharmacies must be making the driver wonder. What if he tells the police? I start a conversation with him, give him some rigmarole about the two of us

3. Fallada wrote '80' in figures.

being not exactly dentists but sort of dental technicians. And as such we aren't supplied with anaesthetics for pain-free extractions for our patients, we get prescriptions from dentists, and these prescriptions cost money. That's why we're going into all these pharmacies . . .

The driver keeps saying, yes, I see, and nodding his head. But there's something uncertain about his smile, so I remain suspicious of him and resolve to pay him off as soon as we can find a moment, only not right away because then he'll just go to the nearest policeman.

3

Wolf is back. 'Lose the car.'

My heart starts to beat. 'Did you get some then?'

'Lose the car.'

I pay the driver, and give him a ridiculous tip. Then: 'Have you got the stuff?'

'Like fun! Today's such a rotten fucked-up day none of these bastards is going to accept my prescription. We'd better go about it differently. I'll keep on with the pharmacies, and you go to a doctor and see if you can't steal some prescription forms.'

'Sorry, I can't do that. In my present state any doctor can tell at a glance that I'm a morphinist.'

'Well, let him. We just need the prescription forms.'

'And what will we do with them? If it says morphine, they just ring the doctor.'

'Then we'll take the midday train to Leipzig. Just be sure to take a good stack, enough to see us through a couple of weeks.'

'Okay, I'll give it a go. And where do we meet?'

'One o'clock at the Pschorr beer hall.'

'What if you get lucky before that?'

'I'll try and hook up with you sooner.'

'All right, then!'

'See you!'

I head off. It's not my first shot at a tour like this. I'm better at this game than Wolf because I am better dressed and look more trustworthy. But today I'm in a pathetic state. I can't seem to walk properly; though I keep wiping my hands on my handkerchief, a minute later they're running with sweat again; and I have to yawn incessantly. This isn't going to work, I can tell already.

Passing a bar, I think a drink or two might help to settle me. But after one glass I need to get out, like before with the coffee my stomach is mutinying, I can't seem to keep anything down. Then I'm sitting on the grim bog, crying. As soon as I've recovered a little, I head off again.

The first doctor's I come to, the waiting room is chock-a-block. Panel-doctor, to make matters worse. They issue so few prescriptions to private patients that they usually keep the block of them inside their desks. I decide not even to try, and sneak out.

On the stairs I feel so ill, I need to sit down. I can't go on. I decide to lie here and wait for someone to find me and take me to the doctor. Who, out of sympathy, will give me an injection. At least that way I'll get faster service than if I sit in the waiting room for my turn.

Someone is coming up the stairs. I hurriedly get up, pass him, and go out on to the street. A few doors along I see another doctor's plate and I go up. He's not open for business for another fifteen minutes, fine, I'll go in and wait. I sit there all alone, looking through his magazines.

Suddenly I get an idea. I stand up and press my ear to the surgery door. Nothing. Very slowly I turn the doorknob, the door opens a crack, I peep in and I don't see anyone. Inch by inch I open the door, I creep on tiptoe into the surgery. There's the desk, and there in that wooden tray ... I'm already reaching out my hand when I think I hear a noise, and I leap back into the waiting room and sit down.

No further noise, no one comes in, it was a mistake. But now I'm too demoralized to chance it a second time, I sit there idly, unable to do anything. The minutes pass, I could have emptied the desk, I could have had my pick of his medicine cupboard, but I don't dare; today just is an unlucky day.

Just keep still, Hans, and take your medicine.

4

The doctor half-opens the door and asks me in. I get up, enter the surgery, bow and give him my name. Suddenly all my hesitation and feebleness are fallen from me, I'm no longer a slimy dissolute something or other at the end of my rope, but a calm man of the world, expressing himself succinctly and effectively.

I know I'm making an excellent impression. I smile, I use a racy expression with the assuredness of someone in full control of his language, I throw in a little gesture and cross my legs to show off my silk socks.

The doctor sits opposite and keeps his eyes riveted on me.

I get to the point. I am just passing through Berlin and have a very painful abscess on my arm, would the Medical Councillor perhaps have the goodness to examine it, and see if it might be possible to lance it?

The doctor asks me to take my jacket off. I show him

the swollen, purple place on the inside of my forearm where pus is seething under the skin, ringed by dozens of puncture marks, from angry pink to brownish and almost healed.

He says: 'Are you a morphinist?'

'Used to be, Medical Councillor! Used to be! I'm in the withdrawal phase. The worst is behind me, Medical Councillor. Nine-tenths better.'

'Good. Very well, then I'll operate.'

Just that. Not another word. My serenity vanishes, I stand there pale and shaking, afraid of the knife which I know is going to hurt. The doctor has his back to me, is looking in a glass case for scalpel, pincers, swabs . . . I take one large soundless step on the carpet, my finger-tips brush against paper, and –

'Be a good fellow, and just leave them where they are,' the doctor says curtly.

I'm reeling. I can see the city before my eyes, rushing by, where I am so all alone, victim to a despair that is like nothing else. I see the streets full of people going places, going to other people, only I am abandoned and washed up. A sob wells in my throat, forces my mouth open.

Suddenly my face is running with tears. I'm wailing: 'What shall I do? Oh, Medical Councillor, please can't you help me out, just one little jab?'

He's at my side, grasping my shoulder, he leads me

back to the chair, he lays his hand across my forehead. 'Calm down, calm down, sir, we'll talk everything over. Help is at hand.'

My heart surges with gratitude, in a few seconds I will be released from this nameless torment and will receive my injection. The words tumble over one another, life is already getting easier, I will break myself of the habit, this will be my last, my very last injection, followed by no more. I swear. 'Can I have it now, please, right away? But it will have to be 3 per cent solution, and five mls, otherwise it won't have any effect.'

'I'm not giving you an injection. You have to get to the point where this life becomes so unendurable for you that you freely decide to institutionalize yourself.'

'I'll kill myself first.'

'No you won't. No morphinist will kill himself, except indirectly or inadvertently by overdose. He'd rather go through the most atrocious sufferings than give up the smallest chance of getting another injection. No, you won't kill yourself. But it's high time for you to go to an institution, if it's not already too late. Do you have money?'

'A little.'

'Enough to afford treatment in a private clinic?'

'Yes! But they won't give me any morphine there either!'

'You'll get some to start off with, then gradually less while they wean you on to something else, tranquil-lisers. Then one day you'll take a deep breath, and you'll be over it.'

I picture the bed-leg where the poor wretch kept try-ing to hang himself. The doctor's a canny bastard all right, trying to talk me into going, and then once I'm inside none of what he said will come to pass.

'Well,' says the doctor, 'what will you do, decide! If you agree to let me take you to a clinic right away, then I'll give you an injection first. Well?'

I look away, defeated. Yes, I will undertake to go through these sufferings, I agree to be cured. I nod my consent.

The doctor continues: 'It's important you under-stand I won't let myself be duped. After giving you the injection, I'll keep you locked up in the waiting room while I get myself ready. I'm not going to let you out of my sight, is that understood?'

Once more, I nod. All I'm thinking about is the injec-tion which I'm going to get now, now . . . And then we get into an argy-bargy about the dose, which goes on for fully fifteen minutes, and in which we both lose our tempers. In the end, of course, the doctor comes out on top, and I am to get just two mls of 3 per cent solution.

He goes over to a cupboard, unlocks it and prepares

the injection. I follow him, look over his shoulder at the labels on the ampoules to be certain I'm not going to be rooked. Then I sit down to wait. He injects me.

And now . . . I quickly get up, go into the waiting room and lie down on a sofa. I hear him lock the doors.

5

Ah . . .

There . . .

There it is again. Ain't life beautiful? A gentle, happy stream flows through my joints, in its wash all my nerves gently bob about like water plants in a clear lake. I see rose petals. And again I can appreciate the beauty of a single small tree in a backyard. Those petals again. Are those church bells? Yes, life is mild and holy. Those endless sunny Sundays when I used to work, before I decided I preferred death instead. Getting up at the crack of dawn, seeing the sun on the curtains and the sun in the leaves, and hearing bells and birdsong. Then the sound of a whistle, and across the little square with the feathery acacia trees comes my girl in her Sunday best. I'm thinking about you too, sweetheart, long-lost sweetheart, I have a new sweetheart, she's called Morphine. She's angry with me, she makes my life a misery, but she also rewards me more than I can fathom.

How limited you used to be, woman. I always reached past you and over you, I thought I'd reached you, but actually I was somewhere completely different . . . This girl, though, she gets under my skin. She fills my brain with clear, candescent light. I know now that everything is vanity, and the only reason I remain alive is for her intoxication. She lives inside me, I'm no longer a primitive beast so dependent on sex that even in exhaustion it thrashes about unappeased and wild in its yearning for the other, no, I'm sophisticated, man and woman in one, and the mystical union is celebrated at the point of a needle, there is my flawless beloved and my consummate lover, they're celebrating Whitsun together somewhere under the canopy of my scalp.

I feel like reading, I think I'll read the stupidest nonsense I can find in this doctor's waiting room, and a new dazzling sense will illuminate the high-flown bluestocking twaddle, one advertisement will smell like flowers, and in another I think I'll find the taste of fresh bread that my stomach can no longer . . . stomach. I feel like reading.

I open a book. There's a flyleaf, a smooth, white

flyleaf, and that gives me pause: the cautious doctor has rubber-stamped his name, address and phone number on this white flyleaf. Don't worry, Mr Medical Councillor, it's not that I'm about to steal your book, I would just like to keep your flyleaf in my pocket for a keepsake. Because once it's been nicely trimmed by a good pair of scissors, it'll be indistinguishable from one of those long-desired prescription forms that are good for maybe fifty or a hundred happinesses. For today I'm laughing.

I'm beside myself. I lift my hand a little and then quickly let it fall again, so that the renewed rush of poison into it – briefly interrupted by my movement – can immediately affirm the presence of my possessive sweetheart. The effect of the injection isn't over yet, I can still take pleasure in my life. And for later, for later, I have the prescription.

Then I hear my doctor's footfall. Have I not committed myself to entering an institution? My sweetheart smiles, I'd forgotten all about that, but her mere being here with me means that nothing can stop me or force me to do anything. I am all alone in the world, I have no commitments, everything is vanity, only pleasure counts, only my beloved I must not betray.

And I think how rich and happy I am. Haven't I got enough money to buy my morphine? What do I need a woman for? Do I want for anything? I think of a book I have at home, a book by a Viennese author[4] who fell victim to a similar poison to me, I will read in it about his desperation and his fanatical faith in his poison, and I will smile and know that I am just as desperate and fanatical in the upholding of my own faith.

The doctor comes and unlocks the door. I take my feet off the sofa and slowly and cautiously sit upright, so as not to alarm the poison in me by a sudden movement. 'Are we ready, then, Medical Councillor?' and a cocky smile.

'Yes, we can go now.'

'But one more injection before we go, please, the drive will be at least an hour, and I can't last that long.'

'But my dear fellow, you're quite full.'

'I tell you, it's already wearing off. And when we're all alone together, I'm afraid I'll make a fuss. With another injection in me, I'll follow you meekly as a lamb.'

'Well, if you really think . . .'

He leads the way into his surgery. I follow in triumph. Little does he know me. He doesn't know that he could get me to do anything by dangling a syringe in front of me, but that when my sweetheart is on board I am strong and resolute.

4. Perhaps Leopold von Sacher-Masoch?

I get my second injection, and then we leave. I walk down the stairs extremely cautiously. I can feel the good trickling in my body and the lovely, secret warmth. I have a thousand thoughts, because my brain is strong and free, it's the most resolute brain in the world.

There, the doctor opens the rear door of his car. I get in, and while he's starting the motor and getting settled and fussing with blankets, I open the other door and leap out, because my body is young and agile, and I go under in the crowd and disappear. And never clap eyes on the doctor again.

6

I knew I shouldn't go too far so as not to diminish the effect of the morphine by too vigorous movements. I looked at my watch, it was not quite noon. I thought of going straight to the Pschorr where I was going to meet Wolf later. But right away I realized that that was precisely the wrong thing to do. What if he was early too, he would see I had got some stuff, and then kiss goodbye to any chance of getting help from him, who was hard up himself.

Did I even have to see him at all? Hadn't I got a prescription form in my pocket that could be exchanged for loads of lovely shots? If I let Wolf have that, if I so much as indicate the existence of this piece of paper, then fully half those joys were as good as lost to me already. And I was hard-up myself.

I am sitting on the nicely padded and sprung sofa of a wine bar, in front of me an ice bucket with a bottle of Rhine wine. I have the first glass already poured, lift it to my mouth and in deep draughts I inhale the nose of the wine. Then I quickly look aside to the waiter, see that he isn't looking, and empty the glass into the ice bucket. The alcohol would only fight with the morphine in my stomach and limit its effects, my only thought is to extend those effects for as long as possible. And I had to order something to be able to sit here unmolested.

Have I not delighted in the aroma of wine, as I delight in the girls in their Sunday best, even though I no longer desire them? The aroma, the girls, I'll put them in my dreams, where they won't disappoint me as they do in life with intoxication and sobriety.

I pour myself another glass and ask for a pen and ink. I fish the piece of paper out of my pocket and trim it to the size of a prescription block with my pocket knife. It's not quite right, it looks too wide to me. I cut off another strip, and now it's really much too narrow. An unusual format, where nothing about it is allowed to be unusual.

I begin to get annoyed with myself, I hold the paper

aloft and look at it, put it back on the table and look at it again. 'Too narrow,' I mutter crossly, 'much too narrow,' and my irritation grows. I take the strip I just trimmed off it and press it against the sheet with my thumb, look again and see that the format was exactly right the first time.

I regret my impetuousness, why on earth didn't I wait for Wolf? What do I know about prescriptions anyway? He's the acknowledged expert! I reach for the pen and start to write. The glass is in the way, and I move it. It's still in the way. Oh, I really can't write like this. I reach out for the glass, and damned if I don't knock it over and spill it all over the prescription. The blue rubber-stamped ink blurs right away, all my hopes are quashed.

Discouraged and demoralized, I lean back. And then I suddenly understand what happened. The effect of the morphine is over, my body is hungering for more. And, abandoned by my sweetheart, of course I was incapable of doing so much as filling out a prescription.

I get up, pay and go to meet Wolf.

7

My God, how full Wolf is, how utterly unutterably replete! He's sitting there, half-horizontal, more sprawled than sat, barely capable of lifting an eyelid, dreaming and dreaming. I envy him his dreams, envy him every minute he spends in the blissful trammels of my darling, while I'm suffering inexpressibly.

'Well?' and from my wretched, collapsed gesture he reads the legend of my failure. He keeps it short. 'Hundred,' he says, 'hundred mls. Here you go, Hans. And be careful, don't overdo it, okay? So we get through the day.'

'Oh, two or three mls.'

'Fine,' he says, and he's off again. I go to the toilet, the precious stoppered bottle in my hand, I fill my five-ml syringe to the brim, and I'm happy again, I lean back.

And . . . and . . . I'm startled awake by a quiet rattling sound. The upset bottle is next to my extended arm, its contents all over the floor. Wolf! I think. After all his struggles today Wolf will murder me when he gets to hear.

But already I'm pouting defiantly, don't-carishly. Who's Wolf anyway? The associate of long morphine months, benzene hound, helper, helpee and in the end perfectly immaterial, just as everyone and everything is immaterial.

I hold the bottle against the light: there are maybe two or three mls left. I draw them up into my syringe and treat myself to a second helping, and my blood

sings and surges, lightning flowers in my brain, my
heart and my breath dance together.

The wide wild world! Wonderfully and uncomplicat-
edly pleasant when everyone is in it for himself, only
out to sink his teeth into the other's flanks! Off quietly
to the side the adventures that will befall me on street
corners at night, the walks through cornfields where I
can have my way with girls, the shuttered gates to pharmacies that I can break open, the money messengers
I can waylay. And there are flowers with whorled petals, and shells that sound like the dying cry of a wild
beast and then the wide rushing of the sea and the gulls
dipping their wingtips in the brine, and the brown fish-
ermen's sails and the sonorous sands.

I am everywhere, I am everything, I alone am the
world and God. I create and forget, and all fades away.
O my singing blood. Penetrate more deeply into me,
princess, enchant me further.

And I fill the bottle up with water and hand it with
my smiling thanks to Wolf, and he holds it up and says:
'Three? Looks more like five to me!'

And I say merely, 'Five.'

And we sit facing each other, dreaming, until he
starts getting twitchy and says: 'I want to inject again,'
and heads off.

And then I take my hat, sneak out of the bar and get

into a cab, and the whining wheels take me a long way clear of his rage.

8

Then I got the crazy notion of trying coke. So far I'd only tried injecting it two or three times and seen right away what deadly stuff it was.

Flowery white Morphine is a gentle joy who makes her disciples happy. But cocaine is a red, rending beast, it tortures the body, it makes the world a wild, distorted, hateful place, knife tricks flash through its highs, blood flows, and for all that all you get from it are a few minutes of utter clarity of mind, a tying-together of remote ideas, a lucidity so dazzling that it hurts.

But I did it, and I got some cocaine from a waiter. I made up the solution, and I sent two or three injections into my body in a very short space of time. In those moments I saw the happiness of mankind. I no longer know in what guise it appeared to me, what mask it wore, all I know is that I was standing in the middle of my room, stammering: 'Joy, oh joy, I see it at last . . .'

But even as I'm speaking, I've lost the scene from my mind, I can't compel it any more, and each further injection I chase it with only makes me wilder, more furious, more demented. Pictures flash past me, bodies pile up on other bodies, individual letters in what I'm reading suddenly open their bellies, and I see they are really animals, secret, wily animals seething and swarming over the pages, pushing against each other, making strange word combinations, and I try to capture their meanings with my hand.

But then I see that I am talking to my landlady, I am trying to tell her I won't be wanting supper, in my mind I am forming the sentence, 'No, I'm not hungry tonight,' and I am perplexed to hear my mouth say, 'Yes, I am expecting Wolf later.' And then something infinitely quick happens that I don't understand, I am in a temper, single words get stranded in my memory: 'holes in the sheets – complaints – money – dishwater coffee', a wild fury boils up in me, and I leap at my landlady and grab her by the throat. I push her blond bulk against the wall, her watery eyes are bulging out stupidly and offensively, her head makes a small, vulgar movement on to her right shoulder and she collapses in a soft pile, her sudden torpor pulling her clear of my hands.

For a second I am fully alert, and look around: I am sitting in some banal hotel room, a large, white featherbed is lying at the foot of the wall, where I was only now strangling my landlady. I know I am lost, totally and irrevocably lost if I can't avail myself of this one single moment of clarity to save myself. The only thing to subdue this crazed excitement of body and mind is morphine.

I race down the steps, barge a waiter aside, find myself outside, in a cab, going to the Pschorr.

In the car I inject myself again, I talk with wild gesturings, the driver keeps turning round to look at me, people in the street stop transfixed at the sight of me. I see all this, and I also see that a particle of my brain sees with perfectly clarity, but that this one particle is helpless against the general craziness of my body and mind. I see it is madness to inject more, but I inject more.

At the Pschorr I ask for Wolf, I want to ask for him, my face is an uncontrollable paroxysm of muscles, I strive to speak the few words that my lucid particle up there has very slowly and distinctly prepared, only for my mouth to utter some wild drivel, and the waiter runs away, and I run out of the bar.

I chase over to Wolf's flat: no one home. I rush wildly through the city, here, there, continuing to inject myself, getting wilder all the time. My forearms are ballooning grotesquely, blood flows from the punctures over my shirtsleeves and cuffs, down over my hands. Madness towers menacingly above me, I giggle silently to myself as I think of a new plan to incinerate this ghastly city with its pointless pharmacies, to make it blaze like a spill of straw.

And I'm standing in a pharmacy, I'm screaming like a wild beast, I barge people aside, I smash a window pane, and suddenly they give me morphine, good, clear, white, flowery morphine.

Oh my sweet, now I am at peace again. I can feel the cocaine fleeing from it, there is still a little bit holding out at the top of my stomach like a burning thirst, and then that too is gone.

Several policemen lay their hands on my shoulders: 'You'd better come along with us.'

And I go with them, with very small, placid steps, so as not to alarm my princess, and I am blissful, because I know that I am alone with her and that nothing else matters.

And the long torture of withdrawal begins.

Three Years of Life

1 The test

One morning I awake from the deep oblivion that stood in for sleep in those days. And suddenly I know: this can't go on.

I swallow half a pint of cognac, something starts to stir in my brain, my hands are not shaking quite so badly, my stomach is working instead of merely hurting, but even so: this must end.

By and by it comes to me: today is Saturday, at eight o'clock I have to go into town, to the bank, to take out twelve thousand marks, pay in a couple of thousand somewhere else. After that I can take it easy, I don't need to be back here for thirty-six hours.

And while I drink the second half-pint, my brain formulates the following plan: I'll take plenty of spending money with me, five or six hundred marks. Once I get through them, I'll knock it off. If I bring the other

29

money safely back from the bank, that will indicate a return to law-abiding decency.

Then the standard office morning,[1] and I manage to keep up appearances, as I usually do. The usual small fears creep in: won't I have booze on my breath? Shouldn't I eat a piece of bread – for appearances?

An hour later the car drops me at the station. It's still trundling back out of the forecourt while I'm checking my pockets. Sure enough, I have forgotten the main purpose of my trip, the cheque for twelve thousand marks. I stop the car, we go back, the manager calls out some instruction to me, I hurry down to the safe and grab the cheque. 'All right, Pünder, let's go!'

And always at the back of my mind the thought: if I don't make the train, this (un)controlled experiment is off.

But I do make it, and no sooner am I sitting down than I feel a powerful thirst upon me again. Each station we stop at, I look to see if there isn't time for at least a quick one.

It's seven years now that I've been a slave to one substance or other, it's been morphine, cocaine, ether and alcohol. One unending round of sanatoriums, mental

1. After the First World War the young Fallada worked as an estate manager on large farms in Northern Germany, as here for 'Count Totz'.

asylums and living 'in the community', albeit tethered to my addiction.

And with it, the constant struggle for money to buy the poison devil that's consuming me, the oh-so-clever false book-keeping to hoodwink the accountants, the constant act to keep anyone from noticing. Now I'm on my way into the city, at the cusp, maybe, of a new life.

At the bank everything goes smoothly, they know me there, I get the money, no problem. And in another bank I pay in fifteen hundred marks. That will help hide my traces if I need to flee – after all, what fraudster would set aside some of his ill-gotten gains to pay his boss's bills?

After that I'm free, and take a stroll through the city. The harbour sparkles blue in the sun, people swill this way and that, talking, laughing – but my feet know where to go: they take me to the row of brothels down near the waterfront. They know me there too, and the news spreads like wildfire: Hannes is in town.

Eventually, while they're next door whooping it up, squabbling, showing off, crying, whatever, over champagne – my champagne – I go to the bathroom and count up what money I have left, and I see I've already eaten into the twelve thousand. I've failed the test.

I walk out on the street, to the station. More train rattle. My flight begins. Hamburg. Most of the day asleep. At night to St Pauli. The following morning I fly to Berlin. Let them come for me. After that, Munich, Leipzig, Dresden, Cologne.

Always the same scenario: the poison won't let me go. I am unable to eat at all. Sleep – what passes for sleep – is a vividly tormenting blackout.

Back in Berlin again. What am I doing there? What am I doing anywhere? I meet a girl I used to see. Maybe this time. I put my arm around her, pull her to me, and she says, ever so gently, but she says it: 'You're a drinker, aren't you? Aren't you a drinker?'

2 Unless you like porridge!

Detectives are always saying how difficult it is to appre-hend a villain. My own experiences suggest the opposite: how difficult it is to get yourself arrested.

I walk into the police station at Berlin-Zoo.[2] 'I'd like you to arrest me, please.'

'Why? On what grounds?'

'Because a week ago, in Neustadt, I stole twelve thousand marks from accounts, and that's on top of taking money for my own use over a number of years

2. In former times, one of the main Berlin railway stations, and close to the fleshpots of the West End of the city.

and disguising it by false accounting – well, that should
do to be getting on with! So, arrest me!'

'What's your name?'

'Hans Fallada, from Neustadt.'

The lieutenant or whatever he is takes a long look at
me. 'Well now, wait a minute. I take it you're telling me
the truth here?'

'Of course. What would be the point of lying . . . ?'

He goes into the other room. The only other civil-
ians at the station besides me are a woman in floods of
tears over a boy who's been nabbed for pickpocketing
and a rowdy drunk who claims he's been robbed of
some money. A sergeant is attempting to pacify him,
but he gets angrier and angrier, till the man questioning
me turns towards him – and just then the crying woman
whispers in my direction: 'Get out of here while you
can, you melvin! Unless you like porridge!'

And everything goes on, the questioning, the crying,
the muttering of the drunk, while I consider what
'melvin' and 'porridge' might mean. Eventually I will
have three years in which to learn that a 'melvin' is a fool,
and that 'porridge' is criminal slang for doing time.

The lieutenant comes back. 'They're not looking for
you. I suggest you go home and sleep it off.'

'But I just told you I've stolen twelve thousand
marks . . .'

'Just you and your drunken stories get out of here. Or do you want me to have you thrown out?'

'But someone must have reported . . .'

'Not a word about it on our list of open investigations. Now will you cut along, we've got work to do here.'

'It's not exactly a pittance, twelve thousand . . .'

'I'm going to count to three – one, two . . .'

'In Neustadt, I . . .'

'Three! Right. Scharf, Blunck, throw this drunken idiot out of here!'

So I go.

3 Flying squad

Three hours later – by now it's one in the morning – I'm standing in the Rotes Schloss[3] on the Alex outside the door marked 'Flying Squad'. I knock and enter.

There are a dozen or so men seated round a big table. Some of them are reading, some are talking, most are smoking, and all of them are looking bored. I walk up to them and say: 'I'd like to be arrested, please. I've embezzled twenty or thirty thousand marks.'

3. 'Red château', jocular name for the police HQ on the Alexanderplatz, the third largest structure in Berlin when it was built in 1890.

They all turn towards me and take me in. Then, apparently spontaneously, without looking at each other, they seem to come to some consensus. They go back to reading the paper, chatting, smoking, being bored, and only one of them, with a straggly grey moustache, says to me: 'I think you must have had a few too many.'

Don't explain, I think, and I say: 'You know, sometimes you need a drink to get your courage up.'

'True enough,' he agrees, looks at me again, and then asks me for name, address, type of crime. My answers seem to satisfy him, because he says to one of the others: 'Willi, will you go through the wanted list for me.'

'I'm not on it.'

'Oh? What makes you so sure? Do you think Count Totz is happy to let you have thirty thousand of his marks?'

I tell him what happened with the police at the station.

'Well, sit here a minute then.' And he and Willi both go next door.

I sit there on my own, not bothered by anyone. I get up, stretch my legs, fish a cigarette out of my pocket, the last one, and light it. Take a couple more steps, till I'm standing by the door. I look round: they're all still reading, drowsing, bored.

I push the door open, not especially cautiously, just

the way anyone might open a door, and stand out in the passage. The door shuts after me, I walk on, I'm out on the pavement, no one stops me. And then I turn and go back inside.

The grey moustache returns. 'I've just called our boys at the Zoo. It seems you really did put in an appearance there.'

For the second time, everyone turns and stares at me. The fact that I was truthful, and that I am presenting myself for arrest a second time, is enough, it seems, to change me from a pig-headed drunk wasting police time to a subject of interest. I am brought a chair, a packet of cigarettes is put out on the table, they want to take a statement from me.

But first of all it's: 'Empty your pockets on the table!'

I do so. Predictably, it's my purse and my wallet that provoke the most interest. Then consternation: 'Is that all the money you have?'

There are seven marks twenty pfennigs lying on the table.

'So that's why you've come to us! Because you've run out of ideas!'

Interest in me is gone again, the cigarettes are taken away ('you've smoked enough for the next few years'),

the statement is taken in next to no time, and by two
o'clock I'm in the cell, duly arrested.

4 Bedbugs

My first sense on awakening is that I must still be
dreaming. Right in front of my eyes, so close that they
seem monstrously large, are two broad, brownish,
armoured insects. My head jerks back, I feel a horrible
itching on my face and arms and I think: bedbugs.

So far I've only ever seen them on posters for insect
powder, but the light that falls through the opaque glass
in the cell door puts it beyond doubt: bedbugs. I squash
them. They leave big bloodstains on the coverlet. After
that I see the blackish-brown stains on the walls in a
new light. These are no stray individuals, these are the
advance guard of a considerable army with which I will
have to get to grips.

My first feeling is indignation. They can be as rigor-
ous as they like in prison, with rules against everything
under the sun, but bedbugs surely aren't on any legitim-
ate roster of penalties. I'm going to complain about this
in the morning.

I go back to sleep, but it's not long before I'm woken

by a new stabbing pain. The bedbugs are back. I try and sleep once or twice more, but in the end I'm driven to get up, crawl into my clothes and walk up and down, waiting for it to get light.

The second the key turns in the lock, I make my report: 'There are bedbugs here!'

'Bedbugs, eh?' comes a return question. 'Your predecessor never complained about them. Tell the duty officer, and he'll give you something.'

Since I don't know who the duty officer is, I repeat my complaint each time someone opens the door, maybe twenty times. I'm not given any insect powder. When it's dark again, and the place is quiet, I bang dementedly on the door. An indignant voice outside gruffs: 'Shut up in there! What's the matter?'

'Where's my insecticide!'

'Tell them tomorrow when they unlock the door. And now pipe down, or else I'll have you put in a punishment cell.'

'I want a different cell then.'

'They're all full,' and the fellow shuffles off. I spend another night pacing up and down, livid, freezing.

The next morning I make my indignant report.

'Oh, you and your bedbugs! You obviously weren't ever in the trenches!' But I am given my insecticide. A trusty comes along with a white, acrid fluid in a spittoon, with a brush to apply it. 'There you are. Now keep your cell nice and clean, and paint this on against the bedbugs. That'll keep you out of trouble.'

I'm on my own again. And I've got a job to do. I strip the bed and inspect the mattress and bolster. In some little crannies there are five or six of them, and I smoosh them before they can run off. Full-grown, they are reddish-brown, the little ones are a sort of whitish-yellow aspic colour. Then there's the pallet itself. I pull out the cross-struts, paint everything out, drive the brush deep into the cracks. They flee. I slaughter them. I want a decent night's sleep at last.

I go to bed early, so as to be nice and sharp for when my case comes up. I am awakened by the now familiar stabbing pain, followed immediately by itching. My day's work seems to have been in vain, the bedbugs are out in force.

The worst of it is that for some reason there is no light on in my cell tonight. I begin to wonder if the itching couldn't be some figment of my imagination. Then I happen to catch one on my face, and another taking a walk up my leg. I sniff them to make sure. The smell of bedbugs isn't one you'd ever mistake for anything else. It's a sweetish smell – synaesthetes would call it green –

oddly like grass. During my test, I'm put in mind of Flaubert, who found this bedbug smell so arousing on Rustschuk Hanem.[4]

It's extraordinary how much those bedbugs get on my nerves. All day I spent seeing the flat brown and whitish forms wherever I looked. Even when I was writing, they seemed to crawl up the inside of the pen. In the desert of prison life, those beasts take on a significance that alarms me. I'm wondering: am I sure they're not a hallucination on my part?

I remember that I sometimes used to feel a similar itchiness when I was outside, if I hadn't drunk any alcohol the previous night. Admittedly, I didn't find bite marks all over my arms and legs when that was the case. But then I remember that a hysteric is capable of 'thinking' a tumour, for instance, with such suggestiveness that it will appear the next day. What if something like that is the case with me?

Vainly I try to comfort myself by saying I've seen the shapes of the bedbugs myself. But what if this 'seeing' is a form of hallucination? Vainly I remind myself of

4. Properly Kuchuk Hanem, an Egyptian prostitute, his exploits with whom Flaubert proudly related to his friend Louise Colet in 1851. The exotic combination of bedbugs and sandalwood prompted Flaubert to the Baudelairean exclamation: 'I want there to be a bitterness in everything . . .'

the appearance of two prize examples on my bolster that left spectacular bloodstains. I can still see them emerging from a crack in my pallet between wood and iron, while I was daubing it with paint. I see them sitting in the pleats of my sea-grass mattress.

But the only way this would add up to proof would be if someone else had seen it with me. And the warder expressly said: 'Your predecessor never complained about them.' I can't imagine a human being stoically enduring being nibbled like that.

Next thing. When they brought me the solution, a warder with the trusty, I showed them my right forearm, an astonishing sight, studded with literally dozens of bite marks. They both looked past it as if it wasn't anything. Well . . .

And this afternoon, while I was writing, I felt a tickling on my neck, grabbed at it and felt the creature disappear under my shirt. I tore off my shirt – I was sitting there in my shirtsleeves – and surely I must have found the thing if it did exist: I found nothing.

While I was writing, two or three of the bite marks appeared spontaneously on the inside of my left arm, with which I was holding the paper. How is it possible that I fail to see a bedbug on my bare arm, which is in plain view as I'm sitting writing: enter bedbug, bedbug do its business, exit bedbug? – It can't have been bedbugs, then, but . . .

Better I get up and pace for the rest of the night. I'm going slightly potty. In fact I don't see why a doctor doesn't come and examine me. Aren't you supposed to be given a physical examination when you're booked? Those are the rules. The ones that are honoured in the breach, as the saying goes.

5 I get my hearing

From hour to hour, from day to day I'm waiting for something to happen. Nothing does. Sometimes, when I'm tired of reading the same newspaper stories on my toilet paper, and chasing bedbugs, and pacing up and down the cell, I imagine I've been forgotten.

But no, they don't forget about you here. Just everything takes its own sweet time. On the fifth day, my cell door is abruptly unlocked. A man stands there in civvies. 'Come with me, Fallada.'

Corridors, doors, I find myself in a room with a couple of officials in a part of the building that isn't prison. On one table is my suitcase. So they've traced my hotel, that's clever of them.

'Fallada, is that your name? Did you sign this?'

'Yes, that's my statement.'

'Well, Count Totz has sent a telegram. They thought you must have had an accident.'

'Yes,' I say.

'Took the opportunity to do a runner, did you? But then, once the money's spent, the little mama's boy wants to crawl into his safe little hole.'

'Yes,' I say.

'Do you stand by what's in your statement?'

'Yes,' I say.

'The first time you've done anything like this?'

'Yes,' I say.

'It shows.'

'He's had a real change of nature,' says the second official, who thus far had studied me in silence. 'Did you buy those clothes with the money you stole?'

'Yes,' I say.

'Right, you'd better take them off then. They're not yours.'

The two of them stand there and watch as I undress.

'There. Now put on the stuff in the suitcase. I take it that's yours?'

'Yes,' I say.

I get dressed.

'That suit's pretty new too. Did you buy that with the stolen money too?'

'I must have been wearing something when I left.'

'Who knows. Maybe some old rags you chucked in a ditch.'

'Yes,' I say.

'Now get a move on. Pack the things away. I should tell you the hotel wants to press charges for non-payment of your room.'

'That's good,' I say.

'What do you mean by that?'

'I want a stiff sentence. I intend to come off the sauce while I'm inside.'

The two men burst into hysterical laughter. 'No fears there! You'll have more than enough time!'

'Do you think this is a sanatorium or something?'

Then they look at me for a while in silence.

'You're not reckoning on getting out under paragraph 51, are you?'

'Quite the contrary,' I say.

'Quite the contrary – I like that. Because I promise, if you do, you'll be in for it. Have you ever spent time in the insane wing of a prison?'

'Naa,' I say.

'They dish it out a bit,' he says meaningly. 'Not something a little mama's boy would like.'

'Don't try and intimidate me. And I want to talk to a lawyer.'

'Why don't you send him a visiting card then?'

'I have the right to see a lawyer within twenty-four hours of being arrested. I've been here for over a hundred.'

'If counting hours is your thing, you'll have your hands full for the next something years. Okay, get back to your palace! Hang on, the hat goes in the suitcase.'

'But I didn't buy it with stolen money.'

'It's brand new.'

'Sometimes I buy myself new stuff, you know.'

'Whatever. Back to your cell.'

6 Chuntering

I spent six months and five days in remand prison. All during that time, I expected every day to be taken to an examining magistrate, or at the very least to be presented with the charges against me. Not a bit of it.

During those six months I was in three prisons and more than twenty different cells. Of course I always thought the change of address betokened some progress in my case. Again, not a bit of it.

But I had time, time aplenty. And I used it the way most remand prisoners use their time, for introspection. For that typical remand sickness of moaning or chuntering.

I was soon pretty advanced. For the first four weeks it was the bedbugs that dominated my thoughts and actions. No one outside can imagine the extent of my phobia. How many days and nights I spent, shaking with rage, running round my cell, suddenly pulling my bed apart, going through everything in a demented quest for the creatures, spotting them on the sheets, the floor, in cracks in the floorboards. How they gave me the slip, resurfaced, made mock of me. There was no doctor to help me against my fear of them, exacerbated of course by the symptoms of alcohol withdrawal.

Then I was put in a different prison, and the bedbug phobia abated. Only to be replaced by other fears. In the yard, where we had our half-hour's exercise every day, there was a push-button with the word 'alarm'. Every exercise time I fought with myself not to push it, to see what would happen. Then there was cell-cleaning furore, in which I would scour the lino floor of the cell for hours on end, slamming it with the bristle brush till it shone. Completely wiped out, I would then crouch on my stool hugging my legs against my chest so that my feet didn't spoil the sheen. Till I spotted some corner that wasn't quite as brilliant as the rest, and I would start all over again.

Others had different troubles. For a long time I had a cellmate, a former officer of justice, who was accused of having tipped off a suspect that he was about to be arrested. This man forgot about his family, his own situation, the approaching hearing, over the obsession with getting the remand system abolished.

His was a particularly grave case: everything that looked self-evident and reasonable and set in stone to him, professionally, looked so radically different to him once he was behind bars himself. Now remand looked to him like criminal madness.

The ideas that took possession of this once-sensible man and to which he tried with endless submissions to convert attorneys, judges and ministers were absurdly childish. For instance, in place of remand prison, a permanent stamp on the right hand of a person awaiting proceedings. While they might be able to conceal it in general by the wearing of gloves, it was to be instituted that no long-distance tickets were to be sold without the buyer showing his right hand to the official at the desk to prove that it was unstamped.

For a time I had another neighbour whose obsession was that there was 'no paragraph' that met his case. To begin with, I didn't see what he was getting at, and because of our continuous invigilation it wasn't easy to have a proper conversation with a cellmate either. Finally it dawned on me that he meant that his crime was covered by no paragraph of the penal code. He

47

went to see the investigating magistrate almost every day, and must have brought the man to the edge of madness himself with his impertinence and stupidity and the bee in his bonnet. I still recall his version of one of their interviews:

Magistrate: Where did you first meet Scharf?

Petersen: I was staying in the Brandenburger Hof, where he liked to drink a beer of an evening.

Magistrate: And that's when you sold him the wood?

Petersen: No, I never sold him any wood.

Magistrate: Come on, man, tell the truth.

Petersen: That is the truth.

Magistrate: But you knew he dealt in wood?

Petersen: Only at Christmas, when everything was out in the open. That's when he asked me to sign the purchase agreement.

Magistrate: Yes. On the wood that you'd sold him.

Petersen: No, because I shagged his wife. But there's no paragraph against that.

Magistrate: Oh, don't you start that again! Sergeant, take the man away.

Of course a paragraph was finally found that met the case, and Petersen was taken down for a long time for illegal dealing in wood. The night after the sentence, he was put in a rubber cell. He couldn't get over the fact that there was a paragraph for him.

The most widespread condition of course is 'chuntering' – talking incessantly about your case. It's only human that in the eyes of the person concerned the most minor incident becomes a monstrous case to be laid out before every official and every fellow inmate. For a long time I was put with an elementary schoolteacher who was accused of having falsified a bond, a typical family story. The man didn't tire of telling anyone and everyone his story. When he had driven the people around him so demented by dint of his incessant repetitions that they no longer listened, he clambered up to the cell window with the help of a table and stool so he could see the wall on the other side of the yard. Then he would bang and shout till a face popped up at a window opposite, and in seconds flat he would tell the fellow 'the whole story'.

The teacher received regular visits from the marshal, as he was called in prison slang, in other words he had the stool and table taken away to stop him clambering up to the window. Nothing seemed to make any difference, even the furious official was given a report on the latest state of the case, the man would jam his foot in the cell door and go rabbiting on and on.

I ran into the teacher later on in prison proper, and he was still talking about his case. Shortly after his release he shot his wife and himself, even though financially they weren't that badly off. Probably he never got over the fact that he couldn't get an appeal going in his case, and saw that to people on the outside his case was a matter of complete indifference.

Then there is a great section of people who don't survive separation from their families, their wives, their children. Especially at the beginning of remand, it's almost always extraordinarily difficult to get to see your family. As a result, the prisoner gets the idea he's been abandoned and despised, there are the most frightful breakdowns ranging from silent crying to wild tantrums. Nothing makes the least difference. It's almost unheard of for a doctor to take an interest. In the eyes of the officials, 'chuntering' is just something that happens during remand.

I have a grim memory of quite a decent official saying to a complete basket case who was crying for his wife all the time: 'There, there, don't take it so hard. Once you've been with us for a year, you'll have adjusted quite nicely, and in the end you wouldn't want it any other way.'

The production of individuals who at the end of a year might *want* things to be different but are incapable of living any other way because they are mentally ill is one of the greatest drawbacks of prison.

7 Robinson Crusoe in prison

The man entering prison for the first time is like Robinson Crusoe caught in a storm and fetching up on his desert island. None of the gifts and attributes he has developed in his life outside are any use to him inside, in fact they will probably be a hindrance. He has to start again. If he wants to have a bearable existence he will have to forget what he knew, and take a leaf from Crusoe's book.

For instance, how to get a light without matches or a lighter. In my first few days I managed to get hold of a bit of tobacco, but no amount of cunning, no pleas, no begging could procure me matches, which seemed to be an extremely rare item.

One evening found me sitting pretty disconsolately in my cell, with four or five hand-rolled cigarettes in front of me, crazy for a smoke, but stuck for a light. I jumped to my feet. My predecessor must have known my plight, he must have had some solution, maybe he had left some matches hidden somewhere.

I embarked on a systematic search of my cell. Miracles exist, you just have to want them badly enough.

On the top of the lampshade just under the ceiling, only reachable if you piled the chair on top of the table, I finally found these three things: a steel triangular file, a long piece of wood with an embrasure cut into it and, jammed into it and secured with twine, a piece of flint. And finally a tin can with some scorched lint.

Steel, flint and tinder – here was Robinson's fire-making equipment, I was saved. I stuck a cigarette between my lips, put the tin can with the tinder on the table and set myself to strike sparks. I got the steel to glow, but there were no sparks. I struck and struck for all I was worth, sweat ran down my brow, maybe I struck two or three sparks but they died before they could catch on the tinder.

It got dark, still I was striking away. It was night, and I was striking. There was no fire. The cigarette in my mouth was half chewed-up, and that was how I found the secret – not of striking a light, not tonight, that took a few more evenings' practice, but at least of chewing tobacco.

The hidden meaning of certain phrases that are still used outside, though they have long lost their original sense, became apparent. In one prison there was the custom of only allowing inmates one jug of fresh water every twenty-four hours. Habituated to two issues of water a day, I had poured away my dirty water and had no fresh. I would have liked to wash my hands, but as the saying goes: you shouldn't pour away your dirty water before you have fresh.

We were given bread in the morning and evening, in the form of a sturdy wedge of half a pound. In the mornings you cut it up into slices for yourself, but you couldn't do that at night: there was a nonsensical rule that said inmates had to leave knife and fork outside the cell door in the evening in a cloth bag. That left you sitting in front of a great lump of bread which, try as you might, you couldn't wrap your mouth around to bite. You had no option but to revert to the biblical action: you broke bread.

But all these plain, simple actions that you learned were only external indications of a wholly new world. You had wound up in a type of existence where you could look to no one else for anything, only yourself. The more you cut yourself off, the more certain you could be of being left in peace; the more you looked to help from others – warders, officials, lawyers – the deeper the difficulties you were storing up for yourself in future.

8 Chicanery of one sort or another

As a rule, the new bod coming into prison for the first time has no other wish than to be left in peace. If he's not a fool, he will realize soon enough that every wish he expresses – even the most natural and obvious – will lead to him being taken by any official, great or small, for a troublemaker. He cuts his cloth accordingly and tries to keep to a minimum his contact with Messrs Guard, Senior Guard, or beyond them the galactic multitudes of master-machinists, foremen, overseers, secretaries, inspectors, chief inspectors and governors.

But there are times when he will have a wish to express. His arrest has come precipitately, he wants to write a letter home, to vest power of attorney in some-one, to request that something or other be sent to him. Very well. He asks for leave to write a letter. The first thing he is told is that he is only allowed to express such a wish at one particular time of day, unlocking time.

He masters his impatience and the next morning asks to be allowed to write a letter. His wish is noted, and if he is very lucky he will be given a printed let-ter form as early as that afternoon, complete with a letterhead bearing his name, details, cell number and designation: remand prisoner. He would like to get a piece of letter paper without this perfectly superfluous letterhead on it that does not concern the addressee and that seems, moreover, to find him guilty before he has even received sentence; but to get one he would have to ask specially. If the request is approved he must, if he has money, get it bought on his behalf; if not, he will have to use the unlovely paper to write to some friend or other, and ask him to send some proper letter paper. Then, in one or two weeks, if all goes well, he will be in a position to write his urgent letter.

Then he sees on the letter form that he is only allowed to write along the lines, not between them, not on the edge of the paper; that he will have to get by on four sides of small octavo, that larger formats will as a rule not be authorized; that he will have to be as brief as possible, and other such ridiculous stipulations.

Perhaps his money was confiscated when he was taken in; then he will have little chance of actually mailing his letter, once completed. For a first letter, the state is supposed to bear the postage, but often that tends to be 'forgotten'. Or his letter is impounded. Then either he will be informed of this – a mere four weeks later, and all the while he's been consumed with impatience for a reply – or else, in the interest of the case against him, he will not be told at all. Both are possible, and he won't know which it is.

Among the stipulations that come with the letterhead there is one missing, the most important: that the remand prisoner is not allowed to write anything about his 'case'. This condition, which is unwritten, merely observed in practice, prevents him from writing to his friends or next-of-kin about the reason for his arrest, the reason for writing.

Take another example: he has got something to smoke, say a visitor has left him some cigarettes. But the visitor failed to take account of the fact that his friend is in prison, he didn't think to bring matches as well. If the prisoner brought money with him into prison, then he's in reasonably good shape, he just needs to wait for the day of the week to come round when he is allowed to express wishes. Then matches will be bought for him with his money and, a mere three to nine days after the wish presented itself, he will already be able to indulge it.

If he has no money, though, he will have to take the route of deceit, using trusties, who are the inmates who swab the corridors and dole out food. He will have to pay the asking rate. When I was still green in prison, three matches set you back one cigarette.

Of course he then runs the risk of being shopped to the authorities, with his tobacco seized and his smoking privileges withdrawn because he has shown himself unworthy, he has broken the good and holy law of the prison edicts.

Another helpful stipulation has it that the prisoner, unless he is sick, may not lie on his bed during the day. By day the bed has to be folded up against the wall. You are only ill if a doctor has declared you to be ill. If you're ill, but haven't yet seen a doctor – and in some prisons he only does his rounds once or twice a week – then you are not allowed to lie down. If you do, punishments threaten, and scenes are made.

Of course all these difficulties – and they are legion – are only there for the novice. The experienced inmate, who has been through the remand process a few times, will know the ropes. He will keep his complaints to an absolute minimum. The way he keeps his cell, receives his meals, talks to the trusties, answers the warders, all identify the old gaolbird whom no guard would want to mess with – he wouldn't want the aggravation.

It's the new inmate who has to deal with the onerousness of prison. More than that: he is often victim to the whims of the guards, who are badly paid, nervous, stressed-out people at the best of times, and who don't mind taking out their frustration on a helpless victim. I can recall one especially shaming instance of this.

The only variation in the endless days of the remand prisoners is the exercise hour. Then they are let out into the fresh air for half an hour where, three paces apart, they make the familiar rounds of the yard. Talking, of course, is prohibited, but everyone, of course, talks. Anyone caught talking gets yelled at, and if he repeats the offence he will be taken out of line and made to pace back and forth all by himself, along some distant wall.

That's the rule anyway, but even in my first few days I witnessed an exception.

Ahead of me was a scrawny little Jew, a dentist, I heard, who had failed to pay some tax and had been sentenced to prison, then paid up – but was arrested before the payment was put through. Now he was in prison, and vainly trying to get information through to his wife as to what office she should go to with proof of payment. He was doing time for a misdemeanour he had, albeit tardily, atoned for, and with every day he saw his small practice dwindling further and was helpless while the authorities took him for both money and penalty.

Of course he was incredibly agitated, pleased to have found a listener, and was chattering away. He wasn't even particularly indiscreet about it; five or six paces in front of each guard he would fall silent, and begin again after that little kowtow. But a fat moustached guard took against him, probably because he was a Jew – most prison officials, as ex-NCOs, are anti-Semites – and he got yelled at.

For the next two or three circuits he kept still, but then he couldn't manage it any more, he had to say a couple more words, and once again they spotted him. He was made to step out of line, caught a torrent of abuse and was taken back to his cell and lost the rest of his time off.

The following morning. My man is walking ahead of me, as before, with lowered head, visibly resolved not to say a word. But that's not going to help him, the other side is every bit as determined to yell at him again. 'You were talking to the man behind you. I warned you yesterday,' and so on and so forth.

The dentist tries to protest, but they haul him off. The following morning the same rigmarole. 'Next time you'll land up in a punishment cell!'

He's the sergeant's bunny, as the phrase goes, and we watch him go, pale, trembling with fury and humiliatingly bawled-out.

I never saw him again. I hope he managed to get through his remaining ten or twelve days. But I'm afraid he looked to me like a suicide candidate, one of those who, for all the talk of 'humane' treatment, just don't get on in prison.

9 Tobacco

When I was arrested that September night and taken to my cell, I was filled with a consuming thirst for alcohol. I had had nothing to drink for five or six hours, and I thought I was simply going to die unless I got some alcohol. I could hardly wait for morning, to see a doctor.

But when morning finally came with its dishwater coffee and hunk of dry bread, I didn't ask to see the doctor. Somehow the new environment had stung me to resistance. I didn't want any alcohol any more, I wanted a long sentence where I could finally and lastingly break the habit.

And that's what I did. In all my time in prison I hardly missed alcohol, and I feel so completely cured now that I am happy to drink the odd glass of beer or wine in company, but alcohol as such has quite lost its appeal to me. I get on better without it.

Instead I suffered a different craving, from the very first day: a hunger for tobacco. It's barely comprehensible to me that I got over a serious addiction with hardly any trouble, but never got to grips with the other, lesser one. Perhaps it's that I saved all my will-power for the fight against alcohol, perhaps it's that my fellow inmates all had the same trouble as I did. The cry for tobacco is the universal cry from every prison, every gaol, every penal establishment, and the desire for it is what drives all those hidden swindles that always manage to get the better of the surveillance systems in prison. All the passing-on of messages, the trading in money, in clothes, in food and soap – all those are just ancillaries compared to the overwhelming business of tobacco.

When I was delivered to my cell, I didn't have even one cigarette with me. Morning came, the hunger for nicotine came, and the first words I addressed a fellow inmate, a blue-uniformed trusty, were: 'Psst, mate, could you spare a drag?'

I had waited for a moment when the guard was unlocking the cell next to mine, but the trusty gestured dismissively, I wasn't getting anything. Each time they opened my door I would try and cadge a drag, and the gestures of the trusties turned to mockery, open ridicule. They pointed me out to the guards as the one who was desperate for a smoke. I saw I wasn't going to get any help from them. Either they had nothing themselves, or they wouldn't give it up without something in return – and at that time I had no idea what I had to offer them.

Those first days in the Alex I met no one, there was no exercise, and I would have been destroyed by my nicotine addiction if, in the course of going through my pockets, I hadn't found a couple of mouthpieces. I ripped a long bristle out of the broom and pushed it through the mouthpiece. When I pulled it out the other end, it was coated with the thick brown precipitate of tobacco. It tasted as bitter as bile, but it was so good, so good that my whole body enjoyed the sticky mess and calmed down a little.

Even then I was cautious enough to remind myself

that the residue in the two mouthpieces wouldn't last for ever. And since there was no way of knowing when I would next get tobacco, I restricted my intake to one of those nicotine-tipped bristles every three or four hours.

Then there was my questioning with the police, which at least had the virtue of bringing almost fifty cigarettes into my possession. When I had to change, I managed to pick two packs of cigarettes and a box of matches out of my valise and smuggle them into my underpants. How good it felt when I was back in my cell, filling my lungs with fragrant smoke, past and future were equally unimportant compared to that instant's joy: prison wasn't at all bad if it allowed you such pleasures.

But what are fifty cigarettes to a serious smoker! They were used up long before I left the Alex, even though I took out the filters and rolled up the remnants in newspaper to smoke. I was soon back on my bristles and mouthpieces.

Then I was removed to Moabit, and on the way I was allowed to smoke all I wanted. There were twenty or thirty of us in the 'green August',[5] all of us excited by the prospect of change. Most of us, along with our

5. A paddy-wagon, like the (in German) better-known *grüne Minna*.

personal effects, had been given our smokes for the move. All of it was going to have to be surrendered when we arrived in Moabit, so we lit up with divine calm and doled out cigarettes with blithe assurance.

I stuffed what I was given – which was no small amount – up my trouser legs into my socks and, in spite of the jeering of the others, I was able to convey the contraband into Moabit. It was in flagrant violation of the administrative rules, but those rules are framed in such a way that a prisoner has no option but to break them. The system ensured that one became a comrade to one's fellow inmates, united with them in opposition to a system that was petty, vindictive and stupid.

In Moabit things were better for me, there was the exercise hour, there was association, and almost every day there were at least a couple of fag-ends that I could roll up into a festive cigarette for the end of the week. And if everything went pear-shaped I would resort to snaffling dog-ends, a dangerous and exciting sport that I could play every exercise hour.

It was like this: the yard where we had our exercise was used before us by those exalted individuals, the serious criminals. Unlike us small fry, they weren't released in a swarm of thirty or forty to shamble round and round under the supervision of three or four guards; no, they went out singly, or at most three or four at a time, under strict guard and (this was enforced, just about) in silence.

These exalted personages were of course allowed to smoke – which we could only do in our cells – and they had the wherewithal too. And since they had no reason to economize, they tossed the ends in the yard. It was these butts that we now collected up, snaffled them, which is to say picked them up casually, as it were *en passant*, as if there was something the matter with your shoe or pulling up a sock. The orbit was invariably soon picked clean, but there were still those butts that were outside the ring, in the proximity of the guards.

And then it was a matter of the enterprise and discretion and sheer need of the individual. The very hardest ones were left till last. When we gathered to troop off back to our cells, there was often a little barging, and you might be able to take two or three steps to the side to reach the precious half-inch of tobacco. And the happiness you felt when you'd snaffled five or six dog-ends! That was an entire cigarette. A day with a cigarette was good, and a day with nothing was bad, it was that simple.

But here too some guards showed their meanness. They made a note of the collectors and waited calmly till the end of exercise, then called you, told you to empty out your pockets on to the ground. Not content with that, they sometimes told you to trample the ends into the ground, lest someone else try and pick them up. A scene like that would leave you seething with fury, harbouring fantasies of revenge and mocking the pious twaddle of the regulations that blathered on about reforming characters. I'd like to see anyone reform on such treatment.

But there was a weapon you could use even against the guards: you simply put the ends you found in your mouth. They were safe there, and in the form of chewing tobacco they lasted much longer. And that was how, in spite of my initial revulsion, I learned to chew tobacco.

10 The sentence

The big day in the life of any prisoner is of course his day in court. Before he finally enters the anonymity of blue or brown gear, and for a greater or lesser time, there is this day which is all about him. Judges, prosecutors, lay assessors, defending counsel, the onlookers in the public gallery, the series of witnesses: they all remind him of his life outside. He is allowed to talk about himself, once again he has a character, everyone is talking about him, thinking about him. And then there's the prospect of the struggle for those who have some hope of being acquitted.

On that March day, there were three of us awaiting trial. We were introduced in the presence of the warden, we were dressed, we got given our civilian clothes back. Oh, the feeling of a proper suit, after your baggy prison gear!

In the last few weeks, ever since I'd known the date of my hearing, I had one grave worry: in the time I'd spent in my own clothes in the Alex and in Moabit, my white stiff collar had turned black. An appeal to have it washed at my expense in time for the hearing was turned down. 'Don't worry, we'll provide you with a scarf.'

Now, I really didn't want to show up in front of people who had known me in my past life in a blue-chequered prison scarf. But I wasn't a complete novice at this stage either. I got hold of my trusty, informed him of the size and shape of the collar, and from some corner of the prison, from a man I never saw, and through a whole chain of middlemen, I was given exactly the collar I wanted: pristine white. It wasn't the cheapest collar in the world, it set me back two packets of tobacco and three rolls of chewing tobacco. But I got it, just like you can get anything you want in prison if you can pay for it.

In the 'green August' I made the acquaintance of my two fellows, a young man of twenty and an old and steady-looking fifty-year-old. Both were quite convinced they would be acquitted, they were completely innocent. The young fellow, a cobbler's apprentice, was charged with having broken into seltzer booths and tobacconists' kiosks, the older man, a master butcher, with having duped several people with worthless IOUs. I seemed to be the only one who was expecting a conviction, and I got pitying smiles for not having lied about my case.

'You've got to lie. If they put a witness up against you, you've got to deny you've ever seen him. At the very least you'll get a lighter sentence.'

'If we only knew if the judge had a good breakfast.'

'It's all a matter of that. And if his old lady cut him some slack in bed.'

'I'm first up,' said the butcher. 'Hope to God I don't get Jürss! Jürss always gives a stiff sentence.'

'Oh, that's nothing. In Reichenbach we had a judge who was permanently pissed. Once by accident he sentenced a witness instead of an accused. There was nothing to be done about it. A sentence stands . . .'

'Now hang on a minute . . .'

Animated debate as to whether that was even possible.

We reach the holding cell of the court. A bare room,

with just a bench along one wall. The walls themselves covered with scribbles. The butcher runs up and down. 'If only I knew how much time I had left. I need to have a shit . . .'

'Wait a bit,' I suggest. 'When you're brought in, tell the guard.'

'I can't wait. I'm desperate. I need a shit.'

We bang on the iron-reinforced door. The long corridor outside echoes with it. No one comes. When we turn around, we see the butcher has unbuttoned his trousers. He is squatting down in the corner.

'Wait!' I yell. 'Not on the bare floor! Here's a newspaper.'

I barely manage to push it under him. Already he's squittering and farting away. The butcher has gone deathly pale. He keeps mumbling: 'I hope he's had a proper breakfast! If only he's had a hearty breakfast!'

The cobbler and I exchange glances. Finally the stream dries up. The paper is bundled up and pushed, not very successfully, into the air vent. The stink is godawful.

'You are scared, aren't you,' says the cobbler provokingly. 'It's nice of you to share that with us, and all.'

The butcher says nothing, glowers, runs back and forth, pale, mumbling.

'I thought you were innocent,' I say. 'You're going to be acquitted?'

'What if he hasn't had a good breakfast?' he mumbles. 'Oh my God, what do I do then? What do I do?'

Finally the guard comes. 'All right, Rudszki, your turn. Oh, Jesus Christ, the smell in here!'

'Couldn't you, er, unlock the window?'

'The window stays locked at all times.'

a little history

Penguin Modern Classics were launched in 1961, and have been shaping the reading habits of generations ever since.

The list began with distinctive grey spines and evocative pictorial covers – a look that, after various incarnations, continues to influence their current design – and with books that are still considered landmark classics today.

Penguin Modern Classics have caused scandal and political change, inspired great films and broken down barriers, whether social, sexual or the boundaries of language itself. They remain the most provocative, groundbreaking, exciting and revolutionary works of the last 100 years (or so).

In 2011, on the fiftieth anniversary of the Modern Classics, we're publishing fifty Mini Modern Classics: the very best short fiction by writers ranging from Beckett to Conrad, Nabokov to Saki, Updike to Wodehouse. Though they don't take long to read, they'll stay with you long after you turn the final page.

MODERN CLASSICS
www.penguinclassics.com